SAINTS ALIVE!

A musical by
ROGER JONES

For choir, soloists, piano and narrator
with optional instrumental parts, drama and mime

This work was first performed at the opening of the
CHRISTIAN ENDEAVOUR Centenary
celebrations, 23 May 1981, in the Methodist
Central Hall, Birmingham

TO MY FATHER

Other works by Roger Jones
A Grain of Mustard Seed—On the Life of Robert Raikes
(Published by NCEC)
Jerusalem Joy—The Story of Easter
The Stargazers—The Story of the Wise Men
David—From Shepherd Boy to King

SAINTS ALIVE! is also available on record and cassette released by Pilgrim Recordings. The recording was made by members of St Stephen's Church, Selly Hill, Birmingham, under the direction of Roger Jones.

Published by:
National Christian Education Council
Robert Denholm House
Nutfield
Redhill RH1 4HW

Biblical verses quoted are from the *Good News Bible* © 1976, American Bible Society, New York; and the *New English Bible,* Second Edition, © 1970, Oxford and Cambridge University Presses; and are used by permission.

Cover design by Margaret Owen

First published 1981

Reprinted 1982, 1983, 1985, 1986, 1989, 1990, 1992

ISBN 0-7197-0292-5

Prii

Printed in Great Britain by BPCC-AUP Aberdeen Ltd.

CONTENTS

PERFORMING RIGHTS

For performances given as part of an Act of Worship, normally no performance fee is payable, and written permission from the publisher is not required.

For performances where an admission charge is made, or a collection taken, written permission should be obtained from the publisher, and a performing rights fee will be payable for each performance. When applying for permission, please enclose a reply paid envelope addressed to the National Christian Education Council.

COMPOSER'S NOTE

I have wanted to write SAINTS ALIVE! for a long time. The story of the birth of the Church on the day of Pentecost is one of the most thrilling accounts in the Bible, and one of the most relevant to life today. The dramatic change that took place in the apostles—from being frightened and hopeless men into people who turned the world upside down—is something to sing about!

SAINTS ALIVE! may be presented in a number of different ways, for example:
1   As a full-scale musical, using drama, dance, mime, with costume, scenery and props, etc.
2   As a cantata (or concert piece) using choir, soloists and narrator; possibly with some dramatic scenes or tableaux.
3   As an act of worship, employing some drama and mime, and including full congregational participation, prayers and a talk.
4   As separate items in concerts and services.

The only essential instrument is a piano, played in a free, improvisatory and confident style to give support to the voices. Children's instruments are suggested in Song 3 and may readily be used elsewhere. Full parts for orchestral instruments and recorders may be obtained from me, together with production notes giving suggestions for presenting SAINTS ALIVE! in church or school. Please apply for these through the publishers.

The audience or congregation are invited to share in several of the songs and these should, wherever possible, be rehearsed immediately prior to the performance.

I wish to thank the members of St Stephen's Church, Selly Hill, for their encouragement and help, and the East Birmingham Renewal Group for fellowship and support, during the composition of SAINTS ALIVE!

Birmingham   Roger Jones

SAINTS ALIVE !

OPENING NARRATION (*Before Song 1*)

(This narrative should be given in front of the curtain, or at least with the stage empty. The opening music to Song 1 commences immediately the narration ends)

NARRATOR (Voice 1): Dear Theophilus: In my first book I wrote about all the things that Jesus did and taught from the time he began his work until the day he was taken up to heaven. Before he was taken up, he gave instructions by the power of the Holy Spirit to the men he had chosen as his apostles. And when they came together, he gave them this order:

VOICE 2 (Jesus): Do not leave Jerusalem, but wait for the gift my Father promised. John baptised with water, but in a few days you will be baptised with the Holy Spirit.

(The choir and soloist enter during the opening music to Song 1)

1. Saints Alive !

Words and Music by
ROGER JONES Op. 9

5

6

(SA) love he has shown! Saints a-live!

(TB) love he has shown!

(Am7) (Bm7) (Em)

Saints a-live!

Saints a-live!

(D) (Em)

Let's tell the world we're saints a-live!

We're saints a — live!

(D) (Em)

8

Saints a-live!

(Soloists - 2nd time only – Oh, tell the world a-bout it.) Saints a-live!

(D)

(Soloists - Oh, have you heard a-bout it?) Saints a-live!

(Soloists - Oh, don't you care a-bout it?)

(Em)

Let's tell the world we're saints a-live!   Let's tell the world we're saints a-live!

We're saints a – live!   We're saints a –

(D)   (Em)   (D)

9

10

Jes-us! ____ His Spir-it gives us li - ber - ty! Ah ____

v.1.Solo(ists) The liv-ing Word,
v.2. TB   The Spir-it came,

C   D7   G7   C

We call him Lord,   He came in love in-to this dark, lost world.   He gave us light,
In Jes-us' name,   In - to our lives to set our hearts a - flame.   He brought us power,

E   F   C   E7
D.S.(Bar 10)

1st time   2nd time

We're saints a - live!   The Lord is -live!
                            (+Full Choir)

In him we shine!   We're saints a - live!   The Lord is -live!   D.S.(Bar 10)
He gave us life!   (+Full Choir)

Am   F   G7   C   C
                                   (Capo back
                                   on 1st fret)

11

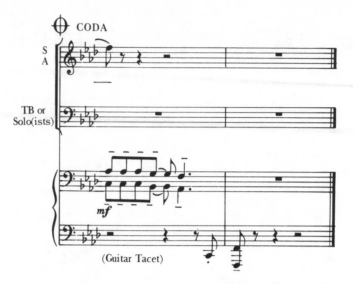

(Guitar Tacet)

NARRATION *(Between Songs 1 and 2)*

NARRATOR (Voice 1): When the apostles met together with Jesus, they asked him, 'Lord, will you at this time give the Kingdom back to Israel?' Jesus said to them,

VOICE 2 (Jesus): The times and occasions are set by my Father's own authority, and it is not for you to know when they will be. But when the Holy Spirit comes upon you, you will be filled with power, and you will be witnesses for me in Jerusalem, in all Judaea and Samaria, and to the ends of the earth.

NARRATOR: After saying this, he was taken up to heaven as they watched him, and a cloud hid him from their sight.

ALTERNATIVE DRAMA AND MIME

(The apostles and Jesus enter)

PETER: Lord, will you at this time give the Kingdom back to Israel?

JESUS: The times and occasions are set by my Father's own authority, and it is not for you to know when they will be. But when the Holy Spirit comes upon you, you will be filled with power . . . *(The apostles appear more and more amazed and begin to speak amongst themselves as if discussing what Jesus means)* and you will be witnesses for me in Jerusalem, in all Judaea and Samaria, and to the ends of the earth. *(The apostles continue to speak amongst themselves, forming a group in front of Jesus, who quietly and slowly exits. The apostles direct their gaze above the audience)*

NARRATOR (Voice 1): As they watched, he was lifted up, and a cloud removed him from their sight.

JAMES: I can't see him any more.

PETER *(dejectedly)*: So that's it, then. It's all over. *(The apostles continue to look bewildered. Two men enter, dressed in white. John notices, and eventually alerts the others)*

JOHN *(tremblingly)*: Look!

(Music for Song 2 begins)

TWO MEN *(in unison)*: Galileans, why stand there gazing into heaven? This Jesus, who has been taken away from you up to heaven, will come in the same way as you have seen him go.

12

2. Power to be witnesses

(The disciples recall Jesus' promise)

Andante ritmico - Maestoso

Solo(s)

Angel
Disciples

1. Why stand there gaz-ing in-to heav-en, ___ Fear on _ your
2. Jes - us, he told us of the Spir-it, ___ How he _ would

fac-es, all a - lone? Jes-us will come to you, You
teach us all that's true, That he would live in-side us,

14

do my works, and great-er ones than these __ For my Spir-it comes in

power to set you free.

(Inst. Interlude)

G   B7   Em   Am7

D7   G   (Guitar Tacet)   G   C

G   (Guitar Tacet)   G   C   F   D

Am   G   B7   Em   Am   D7

15

(Full Choir + Audience)

Power to be wit-ness-es_ to me.

Power that will make the peop-le see _____ That you can

do my works, and greater ones than these; — For my Spir-it comes in

16

And all nat-ions soon will hear a-bout my love.'

Em   Am   D   G

f (Full choir + Audience)

Power   to   be   wit - ness-es ___ to   me.

(Guitar Tacet)   G   C   G

Power   that will make the peop-le   see ___

(Guitar Tacet)   G   C   F   D7

18

That you can do my works, And great-er ones than these, _ For my

Spir-it comes in power to set you free, For my

Spir-it comes in power to set you free!

19

NARRATION *(Between Songs 2 and 3)*

NARRATOR: Then the apostles went back to Jerusalem from the Mount of Olives. They entered the city and went up to the room where they were staying: Peter, John, James and Andrew, Philip and Thomas, Bartholomew and Matthew, James son of Alphaeus, Simon the Patriot, and Judas son of James. They gathered frequently to pray as a group, together with the women and with Mary the mother of Jesus and with his brothers.

OPTIONAL DRAMA *(To follow above narration)*

(Enter apostles and women, deep in conversation)

WOMAN 1: But don't you see, Jesus has gone! *(Despairingly)* He showed us how to live, he told us what to do, but without him around to guide us and give us his power, how can we do it?

WOMAN 2 *(gloomily):* I know that no matter how hard I try, I can never do the things he did.

JOHN: But that's just it—he said we could! Don't you remember, Peter? Jesus said, 'Whoever believes in me will do what I do—even greater things—because I am going to the Father.'

JAMES: And that is what has happened! *(Turns to John)* Surely you remember, John? You were sitting by his side when he said, 'When I go, you will not be left alone; I will come back to you.'

JOHN: Yes, I remember now; and he also said, 'I will ask the Father, and he will give you another Helper, who will stay with you for ever . . .' *(John pauses, trying to remember the rest)*

PETER *(continuing John's line, thoughtfully)* '. . . the Spirit who reveals the truth about God. The world cannot receive him, because it cannot see him or know him. But you know him, because he remains with you and is in you.' *(Exclaims to all)* Jesus is going to come and live in us, by the Holy Spirit.

(General sounds of agreement amongst apostles and women. Woman 1 comes forward)

WOMAN 1: That's all very well, but what do we do now?

PETER *(with confidence):* We do what he told us to do. Surely we've learnt that much!

WOMAN 2: What do you mean, Peter?

PETER: He said we must wait in the city until the power from above comes down on us. *(Peter waits while the apostles remember Jesus' words)* Come on, let's pray! *(The apostles and women gather into groups for prayer. Song 3 begins)*

3. Breathe on me

(The disciples gather together to pray and wait)

Allegretto grazioso

(1st verse - Soloists) 1. Breathe on me, Breath of God,_ Fill me with
(2nd verse - Full Choir) 2. Breathe on me, Breath of God,_ Blend all my

(Capo on 4)

life a - new,_ That I may love what thou_ dost love, And do what
soul with thine,_ Un - til this earth - ly part of me, Glows with thy

thou wouldst do._ Breathe on me, Breath of God,_ Un - til my
fire div - ine._ Breathe on me, Breath of God,_ So shall I

21

heart is pure,_ Un-til with thee I will_ one will To do and to en-
nev-er die,_ But live with thee the per-fect life Of thine et-er-nit-

(C)   (F)   (Em) (C) (Am) (D̄9)   (G7)

1st time
2nd time

- dure,
        - y

(C)   (Dm7) (G7)

Improvisatory Section
against Narration (see next page)

(S) Ah

p
(A)   Ah
(⊝)

p

(TB) Ah

Tempo rubato

p

22

These bars should be repeated
for as long as necessary whilst
Narration lasts.

NARRATION *(During improvisatory section)*

NARRATOR (Voice 1): When the day of Pentecost came, all the believers were gathered together in one place. Suddenly there was a noise from the sky which sounded like a strong wind blowing, and it filled the whole house where they were sitting. Then they saw what looked like tongues of fire which spread out and touched each person there. They were all filled with the Holy Spirit and began to talk in other languages, as the Spirit enabled them to speak.

The voice and piano parts shown on page 22 are intended merely as suggestions for the accompaniment of the narration. The piano accompaniment should continue throughout, and the following suggested instrumental fragments may be added at the appropriate times.

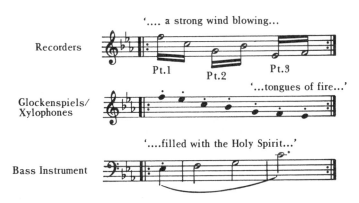

When the narration is completed all parts should continue to a climax and then fade. To simulate the effect of speaking in other languages, the following words should be sung by the choir or individuals, repeating the phrases several times. Alternatively, prayers or any other suitable act of worship may be included at this point.

To be sung
once the
Narration has
finished

S: We praise you, Lord, for you are great!

A: We thank you, Father.
We thank you, Jesus.
We thank you, Spirit.

T/B: The Lord is King!
here!

As the parts fade, or at the conclusion of worship, and at the guidance of the director or conductor, the instruments followed by the choir should introduce the following chorus, which may later be repeated by the audience/congregation.

1st time - instruments only   2nd time + choir   3rd time + audience / congregation

We praise you, Lord, for what you've done! For the

Piano continues
similarly throughout

great things you've ac-com-plished through your Son! We praise you, Fath-er! We praise you,

Jes - us! We praise you, Spir - it! You are one!

At the end of the chorus the parts should gently fade, followed by a few moments of silence. In a church service there may follow a further period of prayer and a congregational repeat of 'Breathe on me, Breath of God'.

NARRATION *(Between Songs 3 and 4)*

NARRATOR (Voice 1): There were Jews living in Jerusalem, religious men who had come from every country in the world. When they heard this noise, a large crowd gathered. They were all excited, because each one of them heard the believers speaking in his own language. Amazed and confused, they kept asking each other, 'What does this mean?' But others made fun of the believers, saying, 'These people are drunk!' Then Peter stood up with the other eleven apostles and in a loud voice began to speak to the crowd:

VOICE 2 (Peter): Fellow-Jews and all of you who live in Jerusalem, listen to me and let me tell you what this means. These people are not drunk, as you suppose; it is only nine o'clock in the morning. Instead, this is what the prophet Joel spoke about:

ALTERNATIVE DRAMA

NARRATOR (Voice 1): There were Jews living in Jerusalem, religious men who had come from every country in the world. When they heard this noise, a large crowd gathered. *(Enter a group of men, women and children)* They were all excited, because each one of them heard the believers speaking in his own language.

FIRST PERSON: These people who are talking like this are Galileans! How is it, then, that all of us hear them speaking in our own native languages? We are from . . . *(He points to a different member of the group in turn. Each one is prepared to shout out the place name as follows)*

PEOPLE *(in turn)*: . . . Parthia . . . Media . . . Elam . . . Mesopotamia . . . Judaea . . . Cappadocia . . . Pontus . . . Asia . . . Phrygia . . . Pamphylia . . . Egypt . . . Libya . . . Rome . . . Crete . . . Arabia . . .

SECOND PERSON: . . . yet all of us hear them speaking in our own languages about the great things that God has done!

PEOPLE *(loudly in unison)*: What does this mean?

THIRD and FOURTH PERSONS *(derisively)*: These people are drunk!

PETER: Fellow-Jews and all of you who live in Jerusalem, listen to me and let me tell you what this means. These people are not drunk, as you suppose; it is only nine o'clock in the morning. Instead, this is what the prophet Joel spoke about:
'I will pour out my Spirit on everyone.
Your sons and daughters will proclaim my message.'

4. Song of Joel
(Peter's sermon—Part 1)

26

27

S A: smoke! (SA) The sun be-come as dark and the moon as blood, Be - fore ___ the Lord's day

T B: smoke! (TB) Be - fore ___ the Lord's day

S A: comes! I will pour out my Spir-it on all flesh,

T B: comes! I will pour out my Spir-it on all flesh, And your

S A: Ah ___ Your young men shall see vis - ions And your

T B: sons and your daugh-ters shall proph-es-y, Ah ___

old men shall dream dreams, When I pour out my Spir-it on all flesh.

When I pour out my Spir-it on all flesh.

Who-so-ev-er calls on the Lord's name, On the name of the Lord,

Who-so-ev-er calls on the Lord's name, On the name of the Lord,

Who-so-ev-er calls on the Lord's name, He shall then be saved!

Who-so-ev-er calls on the Lord's name, He shall then be saved!

31

5. O listen here, O Israel

(Peter's sermon—Part 2)

S A
Jes - us Christ, whose mir - a - cles and won - ders were a sign,
But the one you killed and lab - elled her - e - tic and liar,

T + Peter B
Lord Jes - us Christ, whose won - ders were a sign.
The one you killed as her - e - tic and liar,

C   C aug   F7   Bdim

S A
They were there as proof of his auth - o - ri - ty di - vine.
God has made him Lord, and he has made him the Mess-iah.   (Peter)

T + Peter B
And there to prove auth - o - rit - y div - ine.   For you your-
He is the Lord and he is the Mess - iah.   For God has

C   C aug   F   B7

S A

Peter
- selves al - read - y know. In - to your midst he came to show You all what's
raised him from the grave, The one who came with power to save, He came for

Em   D

33

NARRATION *(Between Songs 5 and 6)*

NARRATOR (Voice 1): And Peter said: 'God has raised this very Jesus from death, and we are all witnesses to this fact. He has been raised to the right-hand side of God, his Father, and has received from him the Holy Spirit, as he had promised. What you now see and hear is his gift that he has poured out on us. All the people of Israel, then, are to know for sure that this Jesus, whom you crucified, is the one that God has made Lord and Messiah!'

ALTERNATIVE DRAMA

PETER: My brothers, I must speak to you plainly about our famous ancestor King David. He died and was buried, and his grave is here with us to this very day. He was a prophet, and he knew what God had promised him: God had made a vow that he would make one of David's descendants a king, just as David was. David saw what God was going to do. Listen to what he said *(Peter points to John, who comes forward with a scroll and reads from it):*

JOHN *(reading)*: 'He was not abandoned in the world of the dead;
his body did not rot in the grave.'

PETER: God has raised this very Jesus from death, and we are all witnesses to this fact. He has been raised to the right-hand side of God, his Father, and has received from him the Holy Spirit, as he had promised. What you now see and hear is his gift that he has poured out on us. All the people of Israel, then, are to know for sure that this Jesus, whom you crucified, is the one that God has made Lord and Messiah!

(The crowd react in a surprised manner, and murmur among themselves as Song 6 begins)

6. God raised him up!
(Peter's sermon—Part 3)

38

40

41

42

NARRATION *(Between Songs 6 and 7)*

NARRATOR (Voice 1): When the people heard this, they were deeply troubled and said to Peter and the other apostles, 'What shall we do, brothers?' Peter said to them, 'Each one of you must turn away from his sins and be baptised in the name of Jesus Christ, so that your sins will be forgiven; and you will receive God's gift, the Holy Spirit. For God's promise was made to you and your children, and to all who are far away—all whom the Lord our God calls to himself.'

ALTERNATIVE DRAMA

(The people, who throughout Song 6 have become more and more agitated and concerned, move nearer to Peter. Some kneel, others appear upset and console each other. With one voice they appeal to Peter and the apostles)

PEOPLE: Brothers . . . what shall we do?

PETER *(authoritatively)*: Each one of you must turn away from his sins and be baptised in the name of Jesus Christ, so that your sins will be forgiven; and you will receive God's gift, the Holy Spirit. For God's promise was made to you and your children, and to all who are far away—all whom the Lord our God calls to himself.

(The people become still and subdued, and one comes forward, as if to summarise the response of them all. This person becomes the soloist in Song 7)

7. When I survey
(Response to the Gospel message)

Andante cantabile con espressione

(Disciple)

When I sur- vey ——— the won-drous cross, — On which the Prince of glor - y died, My rich-est

(Guitar- Capo on 1st fret)

(Am) (D7) (G) (Am) (B7) (Em) (C)

43

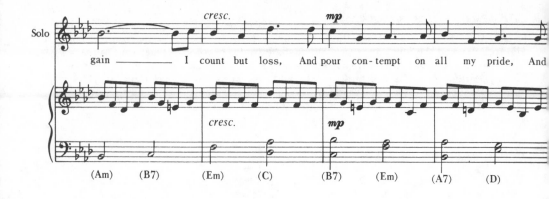

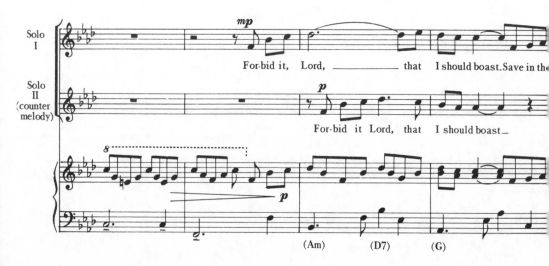

46

Were the whole realm _____ of nat-ure mine, ___ That were an

(Am) (D) (G) (Em)

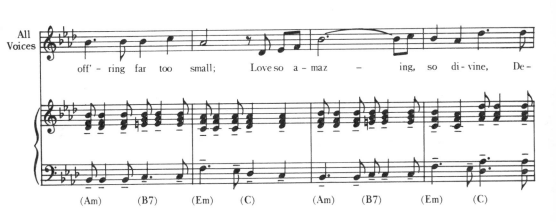

off'-ring far too small; Love so a-maz ___ ing, so di-vine, De-

(Am) (B7) (Em) (C) (Am) (B7) (Em) (C)

-mands my soul, my life, my all, De-mands ___ my soul, my life, ___ my

(B7) (Em) (A7) (D) (C) (Am7) (B7)

47

NARRATION (*Between Songs 7 and 8*)

NARRATOR: In these and many other words Peter pressed his case and pleaded with them: 'Save yourselves', he said, 'from this crooked age.' Then those who accepted his word were baptised, and some three thousand were added to their number that day.

OPTIONAL TALK

The talk should be related to Peter's sermon at Pentecost, and should be given either by Peter, or spoken by the narrator, or an apostle, or an outsider to the cast. It should be specially prepared and relevant for the occasion.

8. Brothers and sisters
(Enjoying the Gospel)

50

INSTRUMENTAL VERSE

Solo Instrument: (Finger snaps) *mf*

(Solo Instrument)*

Choir: Spoken: Broth-ers and sis – ters, broth-ers and sis – ters

(Claps by Choir)
+ untuned percussion

(A)

(F.7) (A)

(D)

* The Solo Instrument here should be whatever is available to make a clear confident sound, eg, Trumpet, Clarinet, etc.

NARRATION *(Between Songs 8 and 9)*

NARRATOR (Voice 1): A sense of awe was everywhere, and many marvels and signs were brought about through the apostles. All whose faith had drawn them together held everything in common; they would sell their property and possessions and make a general distribution as the need of each required.

OPTIONAL MIME *(To follow above narration)*

(During the first speech, four people in modern dress, and the apostle John, enter from different directions. The four assemble in a line between audience and John)

NARRATOR (Voice 1): They met constantly to hear the apostles teach, and to share the common life, to break bread, and to pray.

PEOPLE *(chant in unison)*: Learning . . . *(The four turn to John with hands outstretched)* Fellowship . . . *(They welcome each other)* Sharing . . . *(They offer imaginary food to each other)* Prayer . . . *(They face front in attitude of prayer)*

(The chant is repeated twice with the mime, which then continues silently as Tempter enters, dressed in a leotard, and mimes the appropriate actions whilst the following narration is spoken)

VOICE 2: It's good to give so much money away. Shouldn't you keep some back for a rainy day? It wouldn't really be selfish. *(First person stops rhythm and sinks to floor, facing away from audience)*

VOICE 3: It's good to share your home with others. But it's really yours, you know. Don't let them trample over you. *(Second person sinks to floor)*

VOICE 4: God commanded us to pray, but we needn't be too enthusiastic. Be careful of getting over-involved. *(Third person sinks to floor)*

VOICE 5: Share your food with others in the fellowship meal. But you need only share with those you like. Let the others look after themselves. *(Fourth person sinks to floor)*

(Exit Tempter. Everyone else remains motionless)

NARRATOR (Voice 1): Why does fellowship stop? *(Pause)* Because of sin. The sin of greed . . . the sin of selfishness . . . the sin of not loving God . . . the sin of pride. When sin comes into our hearts it stops our prayer . . . our fellowship . . . our love for God . . . our love for each other.

JOHN *(During this speech the people who have been tempted begin to look up towards him, realise he is speaking to them and giving them new hope, and they slowly rise to their feet, forming a semi-circle with arms around each other's shoulders)*: My children, our love should not be just words and talk; it must be true love, which shows itself in action. God showed his love for us by sending his only Son into the world, so that we might have life through him. Dear friends, if this is how God loved us, then we should love one another.

NARRATION *(During Song 9; see page 58)*

VOICE 1: Dear friends, let us love one another, because love comes from God. Whoever loves is a child of God and knows God.

VOICE 2: And all of you must put on the apron of humility, to serve one another, for the scripture says, 'God resists the proud, but shows favour to the humble.'

VOICE 3: So then, confess your sins to one another and pray for one another, so that you will be healed.

(In dramatic presentation these lines should be spoken by John, Peter and James respectively, as part of the apostles' teaching)

9. You are mine, and I am yours

(Disciples in unity)

56

We have found true u-nit-y, That the world may see. Fath-er, make us one, Join us to your Son. Let your Spir-it flow. May your peo-ple grow! This is what our Lord has said, He who came back

F G7 C Am F G7 C F

C F G C E7 Am

D7 G7 C G F G7

57

from the dead,   Love each oth - er   as you go,   That the world may   know.

Narration / Alternative Dialogue (See Page 55) takes place against instruments and Choir 'Ahs'.

59

NARRATOR (Voice 1): Day after day they met as a group in the Temple, and they had their meals together in their homes, eating with glad and humble hearts, praising God, and enjoying the good will of all the people. And every day the Lord added to their group those who were being saved.

(Where drama has been employed, during this narration the characters assemble on stage in an attitude of fellowship and unity. By the time the narrator reaches his final sentence everyone should be on stage)

10. All people that on earth
(A song of praise)

praise forth tell; Come ye be - fore him and re - joice.
name al - ways; For it is seem - ly so to do.

The Lord, ye know, is God in - deed: _ With - out our aid he
For why, the Lord our God is good, _ His mer - cy is for

did us make; _ We are his folk, he doth us feed, And for his
ev - er sure; His truth at all times firm - ly stood, And shall from

sheep he doth us take.
age to age en - dure. Fanfare - Maestoso

61

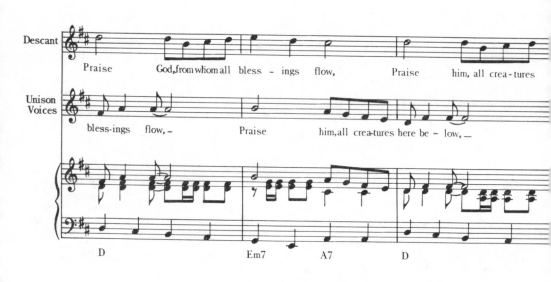